What is in Mum Bug's bag?

Is it a wig? Is it a fan? Is it a jug?

Yes, it's a jug!

What is in the fog?

Is it a van? Is it a bus? Is it a jet?

Yes, it's a bus!

Who is in the mud?

Is it Tim? Is it Tim's Dad?
Is it Tim's dog?

Yes, it's Tim!

Who is in bed?

Is it a cat? Is it a dog? Is it a rat?

Yes, it's a cat! It's Top Cat!